The Mind-Stretching Adventures of Anna Lize and Saul Van Chek

Chance Encounters:
An Exploration of Probability

Written by Norm Lyons   Illustrated by Indigo Prasad

ISBN-13: 979-8-218-09959-6

Dedication

To all of the young, passionate, blossoming mathematicians out there ... keep on exploring the beauty and logic and splendor of mathematical concepts ... you'll be so, so happy that you did!

And, to Ollie and Ruby ... long live dachshunds!
N. L.

To all the young artists looking for their passion and finding ways to express themselves.
I. P.

Smart Anna Lize and Saul Van Chek
Are two best friends who, in a sec,
Will dash from class so they can play
The game they spar at every day!

1

Now when the school bell rings at 3:00
They run outside quite cheerily
Then park themselves right on the ground
And watch their friends soon gather 'round!

2

Their competition's name is "Spin"
And is quite difficult to win
It lets both these kids get their kicks
Through practicing mathematics!

3

Anna has been champ for quite long
'Cause lately Saul's math has been wrong
Today he vows to win the game
And regain his math pride and fame!

Their friends around them know these two
Are tops at thinking problems through
They've been quite strong at math, no jive
From Kindergarten through grade five!

4

To kick things off and start the bout
Miss Anna takes her spinner out
But that's not all, yes, this is true
Saul takes out his cool spinner too!

The spinner of Miss Anna Lize
Has sections all of different size
One covers half the nice, round space
That makes up Anna's spinner's face!

The sections that remain, no lie
Are one-third and one-sixth a pie
A half, a third, a sixth make one
A whole, together, starts the fun!

The biggest section is bright blue
The next size down is red so true
The smallest piece of pie to bite
Is simply colored lily white!

5

Now Saul's is quite a different kind
His spinner, cleverly designed,
Has four regions of different shape
And each is bounded by black tape!

One part takes up one-twelfth the ring
Another, one-sixth of the thing
The third slice is one-fourth the cake
And one-half more a whole does make!

The one-twelfth piece is colored green
The one-sixth chunk, a pink so keen
The one-fourth clump, a deep maroon
And half the circle? Purple prune!

So Saul's spinner is not the same
As Anna's, hence, a tougher game!
Why tougher? Ah, you soon will see
The challenge: probability!

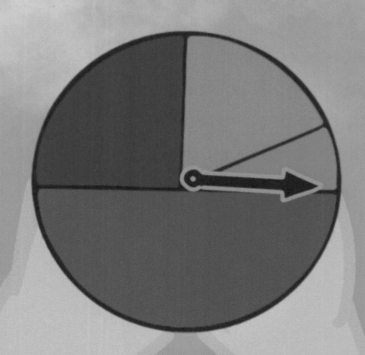

The rules of this game you will hear
Now stated oh so loud and clear
Are, overall, not very hard
And never change in this schoolyard!

First Anna flicks her spinner and
Then she and pal, Saul, watch it land
They figure out the chance its tip
Falls right above that spinner's strip!

Next Saul twirls his spinner just so
Then he and Anna surely know
They must compute when spinning's done
The chance it stops on that region!

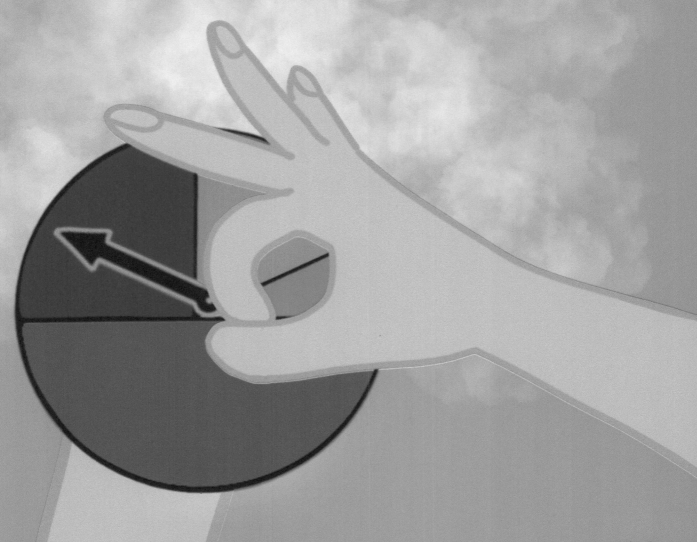

The trickiest part comes up next
It often has these two perplexed
They spin in perfect unison
Then work a tough calculation!

This final problem that they crack?
The chance their two spins back-to-back
Land just exactly where they do
On Saul's game board, and Anna's, too!

11

The first one who can figure out
This game's three questions without doubt
Is, then, declared the winner and
Does reign supreme in "Spinner Land"!

So now you know this game they play
There will no longer be delay
In telling you about their duel
At this game, "Spin", that's oh so cool!

13

So just before Anna's first try
An old friend of hers wanders by
Anna has not seen Ace in years
His math was tops amongst his peers!

This chance encounter? So bizarre!
How odd Ace came back from quite far
To <u>this</u> math game…'twas long ago
Ace said he'd left for good, you know!

14

Well, anyway, Anna is glad
Saul's math, of late, has been real bad
She knows that Saul might need a friend
A helping hand Ace sure could lend!

15

So Saul and Ace play as a pair
This seems to Anna much more fair
All three are ready to begin
And let Anna flick the first spin!

And so the "mathematics girl"
Gives her spinner a great big whirl
They all observe the pointer's head
Stop right above the color red!

17

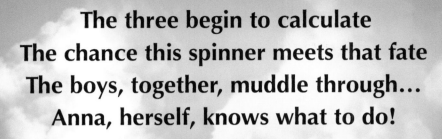

The three begin to calculate
The chance this spinner meets that fate
The boys, together, muddle through…
Anna, herself, knows what to do!

18

Up next, the team of Saul and Ace
Do spin Saul's spinner with some pace
All watch until the tip does stop
On color pink that end does flop!

19

All three, again, do determine
The likelihood of this last spin
They calculate with utmost care
The chance the spinner lands right there!

Now things begin to really flow
It's time to spin twice in a row
First Anna makes the spinner whir
Then Saul and Ace spin after her!

Anna's spinner stops right on blue
This gives the kids their first big clue
Next Saul's spinner stops on maroon
All three kids tally none too soon!

The team comprised of Ace and Saul
Have their solution on the ball
But Anna is of different kind
She deeply ponders with her mind!

23

Each "team" gets ready to disclose
Its answers to its game-day foes
This three-part problem? Not so tough…
The kids just ache to strut their stuff!

The boys' team show their answer card
To Anna's "red" first spin…not hard…
Then sharp Anna, without a word,
Just like the boys displays: "one-third"!

Problem #1
answer: 1/3

Problem One
answer: 1/3

Hurray! They get it…in a blink!
Recall that spin two stops on pink
The boys answer "one-sixth" right here
And so does Anna…with a cheer!

That's two right! Their friends clap their hands!
Next, question three…the crowd now stands
The boys flash "three-fourths" for this part
They think that they are oh so smart!

Problem #3
answer: 3/4

But Anna is a clever breed
She knows the guys will soon concede
Her answer, "one-eighth", she displays
The boys look at her in a daze!

Problem three
answer: (1/8)

These gents think that their answer's right
And Anna's wrong, to their delight,
But Anna, then, does interject
And shows them why she is correct!

Her thinking is based on a tree
A diagram for all to see
She eloquently makes her case
And quickly humbles Saul and Ace!

First, Anna says, "Spin 1 on blue
Has one-half chance!"...Saul says, "We knew!"
"Spin 2?", she asks, "Maroon, my peer,
Has one-fourth chance!"...Saul shouts, "Same here!"

Thus, both kids get each part of this
But there's further analysis
Which this problem calls for right now
And clever Anna shows them how!

She points one more time to the tree
And then asserts quite forcefully,
"Blue and maroon spun <u>back-to-back</u>
Needs a fresh analytic tack!"

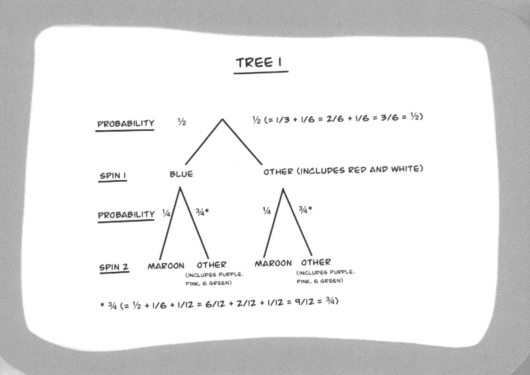

"So take a look again with me
And note the branches of the tree
Possible outcomes for Spin 1
Are 'Blue' and 'Other'...we're not done!"

"The chance is one-half each gets spun...
Now our math journey's just begun
Spin 2's possible outcomes here?
'Maroon' and 'Other'...is that clear?!"

"Spinning 'Maroon' has one-fourth shot
And 'Other', three-fourths of the lot,
So 'Blue'/'Maroon' spun in a row?
One-eighth chance...my next tree will show!"

TREE I

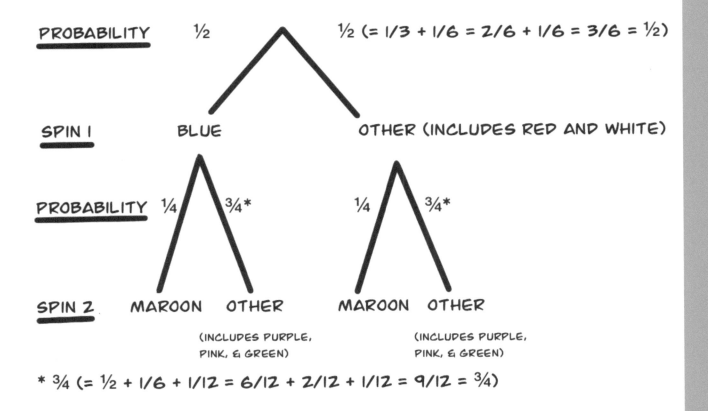

PROBABILITY   ½   ½ (= 1/3 + 1/6 = 2/6 + 1/6 = 3/6 = ½)

SPIN I   BLUE   OTHER (INCLUDES RED AND WHITE)

PROBABILITY   ¼   ¾*   ¼   ¾*

SPIN 2   MAROON   OTHER   MAROON   OTHER

               (INCLUDES PURPLE,   (INCLUDES PURPLE,
               PINK, & GREEN)   PINK, & GREEN)

* ¾ (= ½ + 1/6 + 1/12 = 6/12 + 2/12 + 1/12 = 9/12 = ¾)

32

TREE 2

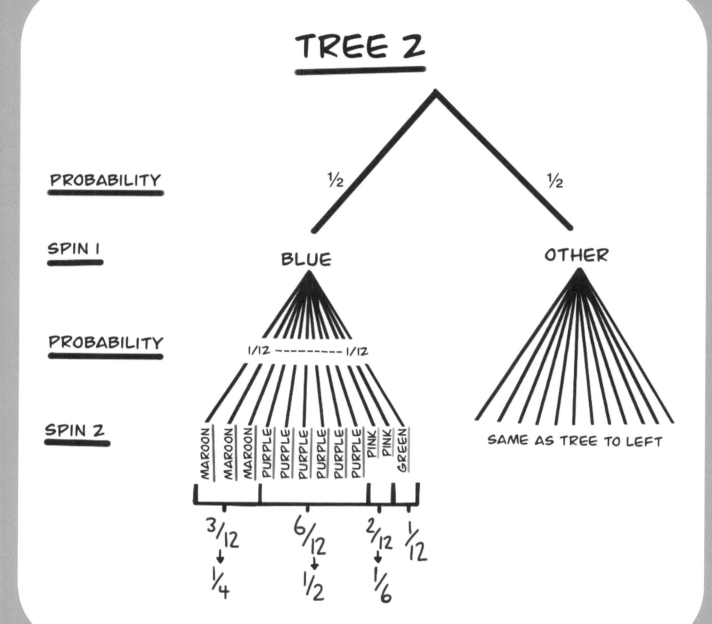

PROBABILITY	½	½
SPIN 1	BLUE	OTHER
PROBABILITY	1/12 ————————— 1/12	
SPIN 2	MAROON MAROON MAROON PURPLE PURPLE PURPLE PURPLE PURPLE PURPLE PINK PINK GREEN	SAME AS TREE TO LEFT

$$\frac{3}{12} \rightarrow \frac{1}{4} \qquad \frac{6}{12} \rightarrow \frac{1}{2} \qquad \frac{2}{12} \rightarrow \frac{1}{6} \qquad \frac{1}{12}$$

33

"Now on this new tree feast your eyes
'Cause we're about to analyze
All possible spin combos here
Then you will see my victory's near!"

"This new tree's the <u>same</u> as the old
Their one difference will now be told
Tree 1 has four *base* branches shown
Tree 2? Twenty-four of its own!"

"Note only three of twenty-four
Possible spin outcomes for sure
Are blue, then maroon! Boys, have faith!
Three twenty-fourths equals one-eighth!"

35

POSSIBLE
OUTCOMES:

OUTCOME#	SPIN 1	SPIN 2	
1	BLUE	MAROON	3 OUT OF 24
2	BLUE	MAROON	= 3/24 = 1/8
3	BLUE	MAROON	
4	BLUE	PURPLE	
5	BLUE	PURPLE	
6	BLUE	PURPLE	
7	BLUE	PURPLE	
8	BLUE	PURPLE	
9	BLUE	PURPLE	
10	BLUE	PINK	
11	BLUE	PINK	
12	BLUE	GREEN	
13	OTHER	MAROON	
14	OTHER	MAROON	
15	OTHER	MAROON	
16	OTHER	PURPLE	
17	OTHER	PURPLE	
18	OTHER	PURPLE	
19	OTHER	PURPLE	
20	OTHER	PURPLE	
21	OTHER	PURPLE	
22	OTHER	PINK	
23	OTHER	PINK	
24	OTHER	GREEN	

36

The boys concede to their defeat
To watch Anna is such a treat
Her logic and her reasoning
Are, no doubt, an amazing thing!

The fellows then congratulate
The math queen who has sealed their fate
Miss Anna Lize has shown these gents
How probability makes sense!

37

So Anna rules yet one more time
Her math skills are truly sublime!
The kids all scream and cheer, "Hurray!
Anna is 'Spin' champ one more day!"

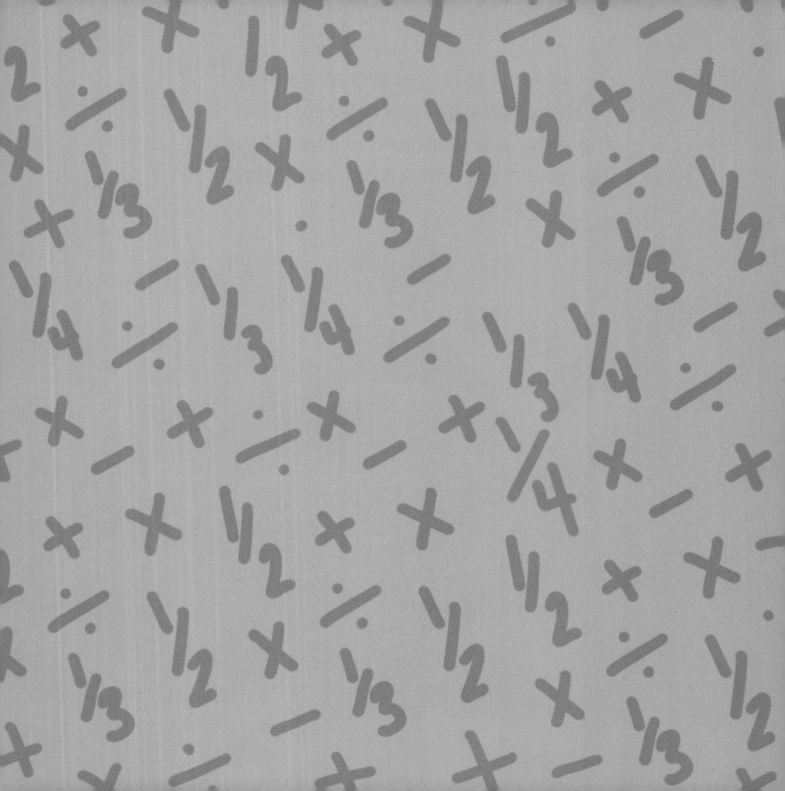

The End